W9-BAA-445

Vera Bradley

FLORAL
PATTERNS

COLORING BOOK

HELLO!

Welcome to our world, where we believe in making every day beautiful.

For over 30 years, Vera Bradley has been known for our colorful and richly patterned handbags, luggage, and accessories. Now, we are thrilled to bring our most popular designs to you as coloring patterns!

The pages in this book will inspire you to create artwork as unique as you are.

Brighten someone's day with a colored note, decorate your home with colored artwork, or even host a coloring party!

Embrace the beauty, celebrate it, and pass it on.

Vera Bradley

40 popular
Vera Bradley
patterns to color.
Don't miss the gift
tags and notecards
in the back of
the book!

COLORING SUPPLIES

Don't worry—you don't need to spend a lot of money on coloring supplies. Maybe you even have some colored pencils or markers at home already! Here are some basics we wanted to share to ensure you get the best results with whatever tools you choose.

COLORED PENCILS

Colored pencils are the go-to medium for beginner colorists and advanced colorists alike. They are forgiving, fun, and beautiful to use. Colored pencils are either wax-based or oil-based. Wax-based pencils are less expensive, easier to erase, and easy to blend. Oil-based pencils are more expensive, hard to erase, and blend best with a solvent of some kind. Both kinds of pencils come in a variety of point strengths. Low point strength means a pencil is creamier and easier to blend, but more fragile. High point strength pencils can be sharpened to a fine point for detail work, but are harder to use for blending or shading. Try a variety to see what you like!

MARKERS

From inexpensive markers for kids to high-quality art markers to specialty markers, there is a dizzying array of products on the market. Markers are either water-based or alcohol-based. Water-based markers are less expensive, easier to find, and can be easily blended with colorless blender markers or water. They're great for beginners. Alcohol-based markers are more expensive and are a little more difficult to blend, but have great streak-free coverage, and you can overlap lots of colors without damaging the paper. Try both kinds! You should also pay attention to tip shape. Fine tips are great for details; brush tips are versatile; and bullet and chisel tips fill large spaces quickly.

GEL PENS

Remember the gel pens you used in school to decorate sneakers and binders? They're back in a totally grown-up way! Gel pens are perfect for enhancing and embellishing colored pieces. They come in a range of colors and effects that can really help you step up your coloring game, like metallic, glitter, neon, and even blacklight-sensitive. Because they are opaque, they will glide right over any base coat of color, so they are perfect for adding doodles and accents. Experiment with different types and colors on top of both markers and colored pencils to see what you like. And remember to give the ink a little extra time to dry—try not to accidentally smear it with your hand!

Tips

- Experiment with other media like crayons, pastels, paint pens, and watercolors

- Keep your coloring tools stashed and organized—supplies build up!

- Add many layers of color to make your art look complex and rich

- Smooth out marker streaks by coloring over the marker with a matching colored pencil

- Experiment with blending colored pencils using a blending pen or even your fingers

- Try layering gel pen details on top of marker and colored pencils

All about COLOR

It's easy for beginners to feel overwhelmed by the sheer number (or range) of colors available in their coloring tool sets. But a basic understanding of color terminology and color schemes will set you up for success! The standard color wheel includes 12 different colors, or **hues** (a hue is just another name for a color—like blue, red, or green). You should know the words tint and shade, too. A **tint** is what you get when you add white to a color; tints are lighter, less saturated hues. For example, pink is actually a tint of red, not really its own separate color! A **shade** is what you get when you add black to a color; shades are darker, more intense hues. On the facing page, you'll learn a few more color terms in the form of color schemes that can help you make color decisions in your own art!

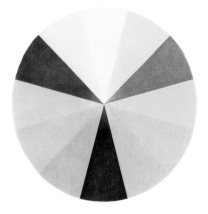

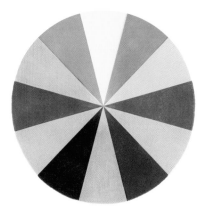

Primary Colors: The primary colors are red, yellow, and blue. These three colors can't be created by mixing any other colors together. These colors are the basis for creating the rest of the colors on the color wheel.

Secondary Colors: The secondary colors are orange, green, and violet (or purple). They are created by mixing two primary colors together. Mixing red and blue creates violet; mixing red and yellow creates orange; mixing blue and yellow creates green.

Tertiary Colors: Tertiary colors are created by mixing a primary color with one of its adjacent secondary colors. Mixing red and violet creates red-violet/magenta; red and orange make red-orange/ vermillion; blue and green make blue-green/teal; blue and violet make blue-violet/indigo; yellow and green make yellow-green/ chartreuse; and yellow and orange make yellow-orange/amber.

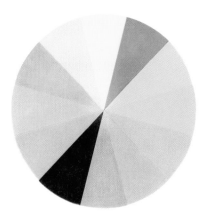

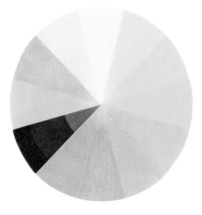

Complementary Colors: Complementary colors are directly opposite each other on the color wheel—red and green, blue and orange, yellow and violet, and so on. When placed beside each other, complementary colors create a striking contrast that draws the eye and makes the art pop.

Analogous Colors: Analogous color schemes use colors that are right next to each other on the color wheel, often in sets of three, and have a very harmonious effect. For instance, red, vermillion (red-orange), and magenta (red-violet) are analogous, as are green, teal (blue-green), and chartreuse (yellow-green).

Monochromatic Colors: If you don't want to think too hard or want to go really simple with your color scheme, try a monochromatic look. Pick a single color, such as blue, and then pull every blue coloring tool you have and color with it. Dark blue, sky blue, slate blue, denim blue, ocean blue, aqua blue—you get the idea.

COLORING TECHNIQUES

Beyond the color choices you make, there are many ways to improve the quality of your work, giving it real depth and complexity. Check out the techniques below for some ideas on how to take your coloring to the next level.

BLENDING

Create smooth transitions between colors in your art. One basic way to blend is to start by coloring an entire shape or area with your lightest "base" color. Then, color part of the shape/area with a darker/different color. Finally, to make the transition blend seamlessly, color all over the entire area with the light base color again. You can also blend using tools like paper towels or a colorless blending pencil (for dry media like colored pencils), or water or colorless blending markers (for wet media like markers).

SHADING

Add dimension to your coloring by darkening certain areas. By darkening the edge of an object or around an object, you can make it look three-dimensional. You can shade by using a darker color or by pressing harder with a tool such as a colored pencil.

LAYERING

Use different art media on top of one another. Whether it's colored pencil on marker, marker on colored pencil, or gel pen on both, don't be afraid to experiment. Try coloring your entire piece with markers and then shading with colored pencils, or adding embellishments with gel pens. With a bit of trial and error, you'll find what you like.

5 *Super Simple* COLORING TIPS

1. **Test and experiment.** Use scrap paper to practice color combinations, test how the colors actually appear on paper, and see how different colors blend together.

2. **Plan your approach.** Every design will have an area that calls to you, so begin there. That might be a central flower, or a striking quote, or a soft background.

3. **Layer light colors first.** You can always go darker, but it's difficult to go lighter, so start off with light colors.

4. **Add accents and patterning.** You aren't limited to the lines that appear in the original design. Adding more details gives pieces a truly personal touch.

5. **Don't stress.** This is supposed to be fun and relaxing! You don't have to finish a coloring page in one sitting. Try working on a complex design a little every day.

LET'S COLOR!

Not sure about where to start?

Here's an example of a way to approach a design that breaks it down into achievable steps.

1. Start with spring green for the outside inner petals and center dot.

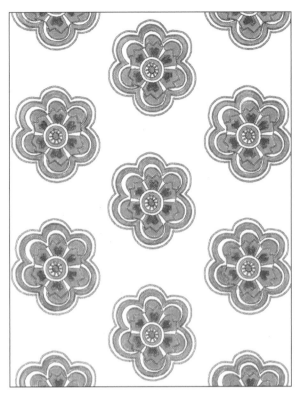

2. Next add turquoise, purple, and pink to the flower petals and inner core.

3. Lay down a vibrant fuchsia background.

4. Finish off the design with black accents.

Colored
ART
GALLERY

Here you will find four favorite Vera Bradley patterns that have been hand-colored by artists just like you! The pattern on the left is colored using the original Vera Bradley color scheme. The pattern on the right is colored using an all-new color scheme created by the artist. We hope this collection will inspire you!

Vera Bradley Colors

New Colors

Tutti Flowers

Love the color purple? Get creative and change up the colors from your favorite patterns to coordinate with your home decor or color preferences.

Vera Bradley Colors (colored pencils, brush markers, blender pen)

New Colors (colored pencils, brush markers, blender pen)

Tea Garden

Explore different color combinations to change the mood of a pattern. Notice how the yellow background here adds a warm touch.

Vera Bradley Colors (colored pencils)

New Colors (colored pencils)

Lilli Bell Coordinate

Outline your patterns in a coordinating darker color to emphasize the shapes, as seen in both of these examples.

Vera Bradley Colors (colored pencils)

New Colors (colored pencils)

PATTERN GUIDE

Use this color reference as a guide to the coloring patterns. Patterns are listed in the order in which they appear.

Camelia, 2012

Deco Daisy, 2011

Bohemian Blooms, 2016

Plum Petals Coordinate, 2011

Flutterby, 2014

Island Blooms, 2012

Olivia Pink, 2013

Bittersweet, 2013

Petal Splash, 2015

Tea Garden, 2011

Jazzy Blooms, 2013

La Neon Rose, 2013

Wildflower Garden, 2016

Go Wild, 2013

Doodle Daisy, 2012

Mocha Rouge, 2011

Lime's Up, 2012

Mocha Rouge Coordinate, 2011

Cheery Blossoms, 2014

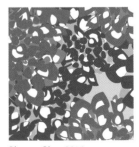
Blooms Blue, 2016

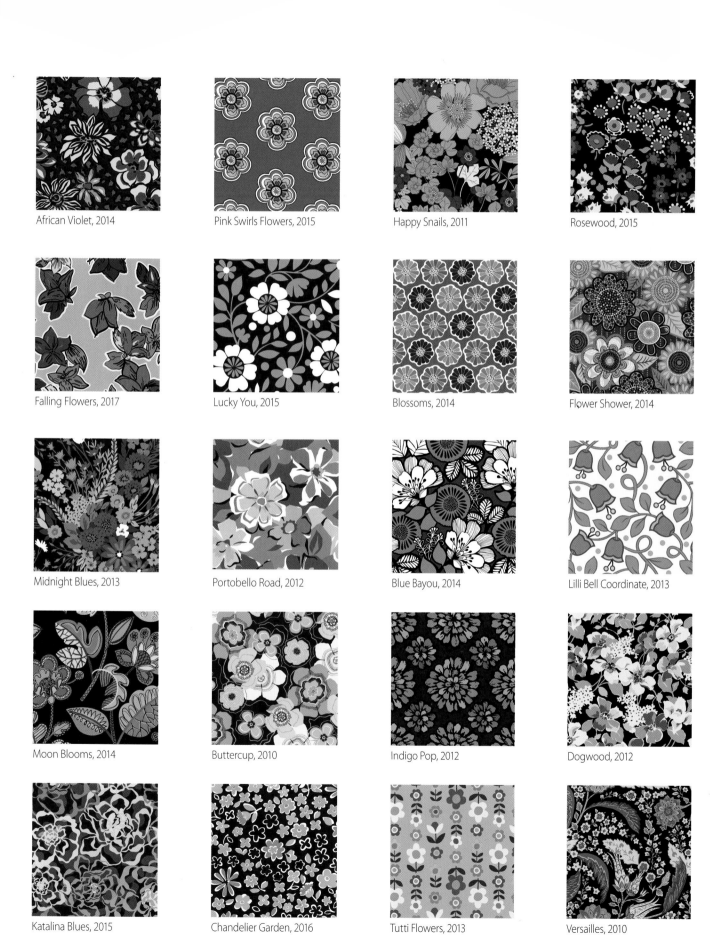

African Violet, 2014

Pink Swirls Flowers, 2015

Happy Snails, 2011

Rosewood, 2015

Falling Flowers, 2017

Lucky You, 2015

Blossoms, 2014

Flower Shower, 2014

Midnight Blues, 2013

Portobello Road, 2012

Blue Bayou, 2014

Lilli Bell Coordinate, 2013

Moon Blooms, 2014

Buttercup, 2010

Indigo Pop, 2012

Dogwood, 2012

Katalina Blues, 2015

Chandelier Garden, 2016

Tutti Flowers, 2013

Versailles, 2010

GALLERY

You can do so much more with your finished colored art than simply admire it or pass it on to a friend. Incorporate your colorings into home décor, gifts, and more!

Ready, Set, Craft!

Check out the gift tags and notecards at the end of the book! Spread the joy with these totally giftable accents. Here are just a few ideas!

FLORAL
PATTERNS

It's time to dive in!

Get ready to relax and let the creativity flow.
Your coloring journey starts now.

Never underestimate the power of fresh flowers!

We are
all different
flowers

from the

same

garden

Always
believe
something
good
is about
to happen

Plant dreams,
pull weeds
&
grow a
happy life!

Even
the
most
beautiful
flowers
have to
grow
through
a little
dirt

and watch them grow!

Daydreams
and
flowers
are good
for the soul

Plant smiles,
grow laughter,
harvest love

In a field of roses,

be a wildflower!

Always wear a smile on your face and a flower in your hair

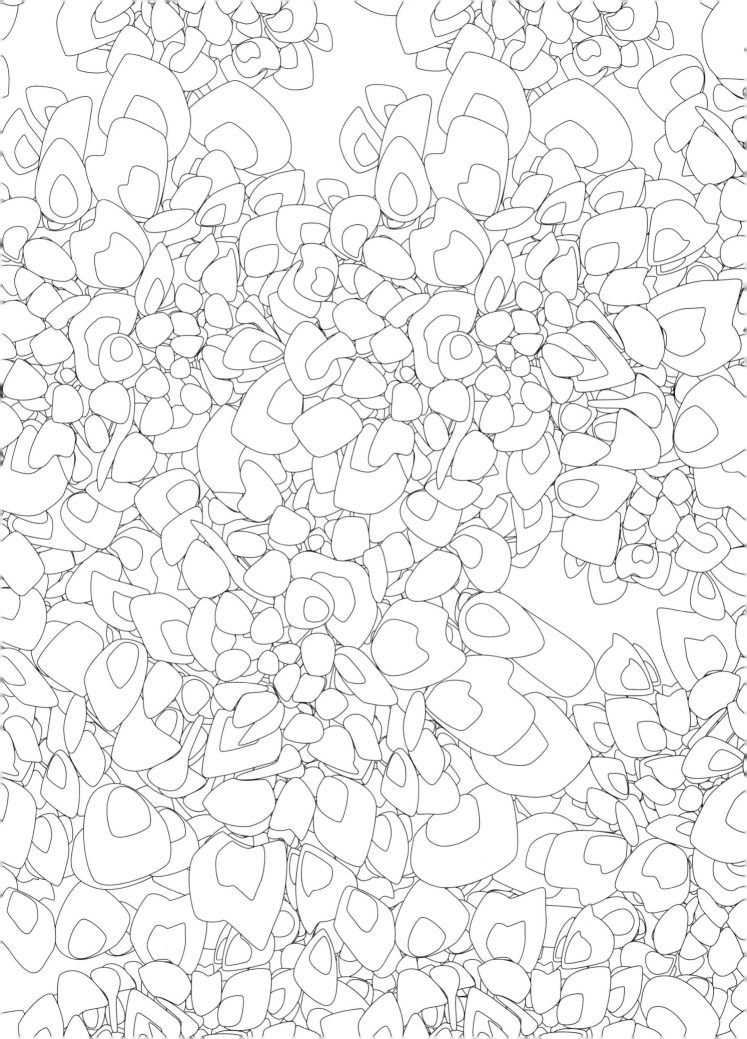

Be the sunshine in someone's rainy day

There's no better bed than one among the flowers

It's a good day to have a good day!

Flowers
can't solve
all problems,
but they're
a great
start!

Be somebody who makes

Be
always
blooming

your feet among the flowers

Live,
love,
explore,
and
grow

When you live and laugh abundantly,
you live a beautiful life

Enjoy

Merci

For You

xoxo

Yay!

Smile

Love Ya

Cheers!

From top left: Mocha Rouge, 2011; Suzani, 2011; Plum Petals, 2011; Camellia, 2012; Va Va Voom, 2012; Ribbons, 2012; Plum Crazy, 2013; Jazzy Blooms, 2013.

From top left: Suzani Coordinate, 2011; Mocha Rouge Coordinate, 2011; Camellia Coordinate, 2012; Plum Petals Coordinate, 2011; Ribbons Lattice, 2012; Va Va Leaves, 2012; Jazzy Swirls, 2013; Plum Plumes, 2013.

From top left: Olivia Pink, 2013; Petal Paisley, 2014; Flower Shower, 2014; Blue Bayou, 2014; Ziggy Zinnia, 2014; African Violet, 2014; Cheery Blossoms, 2014; Buttercup, 2010.

From top left: Petal Dots, 2014; Olivia Floral, 2013; Bayou Waves, 2014; Shower Vines, 2014; Leopard Spots, 2014; Ziggy Zags, 2014; Buttercup Coordinate, 2010; Blossoms, 2014.

Love you more!

_____
_____
_____
_____
_____

Suzani, 2011

Illustration © Vera Bradley, from *Vera Bradley Floral Patterns Coloring Book*

What's up, buttercup?

_____
_____
_____
_____
_____

Mocha Rouge, 2011

Illustration © Vera Bradley, from *Vera Bradley Floral Patterns Coloring Book*

Hugs, kisses
&
birthday wishes!

_____
_____
_____
_____
_____

Camellia, 2012

Illustration © Vera Bradley, from *Vera Bradley Floral Patterns Coloring Book*

What would
I do
without you?

_____
_____
_____
_____
_____

Plum Crazy, 2013

Illustration © Vera Bradley, from *Vera Bradley Floral Patterns Coloring Book*

*Thanks for
being my person.*

_____
_____
_____
_____
_____

Ribbons, 2012

Illustration © Vera Bradley, from *Vera Bradley Floral Patterns Coloring Book*

*Sending
good vibes.*

_____
_____
_____
_____
_____

Indigo Pop, 2012

Illustration © Vera Bradley, from *Vera Bradley Floral Patterns Coloring Book*

*And so
the adventure begins...*

_____
_____
_____
_____
_____

African Violet, 2014

Illustration © Vera Bradley, from *Vera Bradley Floral Patterns Coloring Book*

*Pop, fizz, clink.
Congrats!*

_____
_____
_____
_____
_____

Va Va Voom, 2012

Illustration © Vera Bradley, from *Vera Bradley Floral Patterns Coloring Book*